We write stories.

I was two
the cat ran

We write names.

When I was a baby
by Emma
Up The Tree
by Jason

We write lists.

Our Book Party
Invitation List:
Our Families
Pedro
Mrs. King
The Kitchen Staff
Grade 1

We write cards.

welcome
Come to Our Book Party
Come to Our Book Party

We write posters.

Welcome to class

Welcome
To
Our
Class

Book Party

Printed in the U.S.A.

ISBN 0-439-69300-4

12 13 14 40 12 13 14 15 16/0

SCHOLASTIC INC.
New York Toronto London Auckland Sydney
Mexico City New Delhi Hong Kong Buenos Aires